SHIRE NATURAL H'

THE
BLACKBIRD

DAVID W. SNOW

CONTENTS

COVER: *A male Blackbird singing.*

Series editors: Jim Flegg and Chris Humphries.

Copyright © 1987 by David W. Snow. First published 1987.
Number 13 in the Shire Natural History series. ISBN 0 85263 854 X.

Set in 9 point Times roman and printed in Great Britain by C. I. Thomas & Sons (Haverfordwest) Ltd, Press Buildings, Merlins Bridge, Haverfordwest, Dyfed.

Introduction and description

The Blackbird is one of the few species of birds that everybody can identify and name — the glossy black, yellow-billed males at least, though females are sometimes thought to be 'thrushes' (an imprecise term embracing a group of species) and juveniles sometimes cause confusion. It is an extraordinarily versatile and successful bird, at home in primeval woodland, on bare windswept offshore islands or in city centres, but it was not always so familiar and widespread. Up to the end of the eighteenth century it was a shy woodland bird. Its present success seems to have been due to an ability to adapt to conditions created by man, to its aggressive behaviour, and to the fact that man has eliminated or much reduced the Blackbird's natural predators and no longer persecutes it himself as he did in the past.

An adult Blackbird is about 25 cm (10 inches) long, males being a little larger than females. Its weight is very variable, averaging about 100 grams (3.5 ounces), but very heavy birds may weigh up to 150 grams (5.3 ounces) and light birds as little as 80 grams (2.8 ounces). Weight varies seasonally, generally being high in winter, when fat deposits are laid down, and low in summer.

The adult male is glossy black with orange-yellow bill and eye-rim. The adult female is earth-brown above, paler and a little more rufous below, with obscure spotting on the breast and a pale dark-streaked throat. The bill of the female varies from all dark to mainly orange-yellow.

The young male, in its first autumn and winter, resembles the adult but the bill is blackish and the eye-rim dark, gradually becoming yellow in the course of the winter and early spring. Its plumage is browner, especially the flight feathers and outer wing coverts.

The young female in its first autumn and winter is less easily distinguishable from an old female, but the plumage is usually paler and more rufous and the bill is dark instead of partly or mainly orange-yellow.

In the first few weeks after leaving the nest the juvenile Blackbird is rufous brown. The feathers of the upper parts have pale shaft streaks and the underparts are more mottled than those of the adult female. The wings are dark brown, the tail dark brown or blackish. The juvenile male is usually distinguishable from the juvenile female by its darker plumage, the tail being blackish rather than dark brown.

The Blackbird and its relatives

Before looking at the Blackbird's behaviour and life history, we need to see the bird in context, as a member of a large and nearly worldwide group of thrushes and related birds.

The Blackbird (*Turdus merula*) is a member of the subfamily Turdinae, which includes not only the typical thrushes but also robins, nightingales, chats, redstarts, wheatears and many other less familiar small or medium-sized birds in the tropics and subtropics. The subfamily Turdinae is one of several subfamilies placed in the huge family Muscicapidae, which embraces also the Old World flycatchers, babblers and other less well known birds. Because this great assemblage of birds is structurally rather uniform there has been much disagreement about how it should be subdivided and classified, so alternative classifications may be found in other books. For instance, the subfamily Turdinae used to be treated as a family in its own right, Turdidae. The thrushes and other birds now placed in the Turdinae are mostly rather unspecialised birds adapted to a mixed diet of invertebrates and fruits, and many of them are among the most familiar birds of the countries where they occur.

Turdus, comprising the typical thrushes, is the genus with the largest number of species (about sixty); indeed it is one of the largest of all genera of birds. *Turdus* thrushes range over all the temperate and tropical continents except Australia. The Blackbird is a typical member of the genus, about in the middle of the size range: the Mistle Thrush, another common British species, is one of the larger members, but the Song Thrush, Britain's smallest resident thrush, is a good deal larger than the smallest species which are found in the tropics. Several other species of *Turdus* are very like the Blackbird, with all-black, yellow-billed males and brown females, but they are not very closely related. This is a kind of plumage that is generally associated with mountain forest, at least as far as the thrushes are concerned, so that it seems likely that the Blackbird may have originated somewhere in the mountains of western Eurasia before spreading into the lowlands.

The Blackbird is widespread in Europe and Asia and has outlying populations in north-west Africa and the Atlantic islands. As is the case in many birds with wide geographical ranges, in the main part of its range it is easy to decide what is, or is not, a Blackbird, but out at the peripheries the situation is not so clear, because isolated populations are distinct enough to raise doubts as to whether or not they should be treated as separate species. In the case of the Blackbird, all the populations from the Atlantic islands east to Russia and the Middle East are fairly homogeneous; the different local populations vary in size, and in the south females tend to be darker-plumaged than in the north, but these differences are not great. But the Blackbirds in the Himalayas, where they live at very high altitudes above the tree line, are relatively huge, and the sexes are almost alike; both males and females are dark sooty brown.

The isolated Blackbird population of China is also dark brown rather than black, with males and females alike. More divergent still, the Blackbirds living in the mountain forests of peninsular India and Sri Lanka are not black at all but have sooty caps, grey backs with a bluish wash, and palish underparts with, in some populations, vinaceous breasts. All these populations are conventionally treated as subspecies (or geographical races) of *Turdus merula,* but it is by no means certain that they should be. This account of the Blackbird is not concerned any further with these outlying populations but refers to the main population centred on Europe and, more particularly, to the British population.

Life history

THE TERRITORY

Most adult Blackbirds are sedentary, occupying small territories of as little as 0.1 ha (¼ acre) in gardens but usually around 0.2 h (½ acre); woodland territories are considerably larger. Males and females of settled pairs maintain a joint territory, though in winter they tend to occupy different parts of it and may be aggressive to their partner if it intrudes; but they do not spend all their time in the territory. The nest is not always within it; if the female chooses a nest site near or beyond the territory border the male will actively enlarge the territory, if necessary engaging in conflict with a neighbouring male, until the territory has been extended to include the nest. Much of the food is obtained within the territory, and the owners will roost in it if it contains suitable cover; and most importantly, the male proclaims his ownership of the territory by singing within it. But both male and female often leave the territory to feed nearby, especially when there are sources of plentiful food in the vicinity, such as autumn fruits or worms in an

3

adjacent field, and in very hard weather they may temporarily desert their territories altogether in the search for food.

The territory boundaries are most keenly defended in the early part of the breeding season. The most intense aggressive displays are seen in early spring, when rival males are trying to establish themselves on disputed ground. Where territories are closely packed, as they often are in gardens, aggressive displays and other behaviour connected with territorial defence may often be seen. Sometimes an intruder is quickly driven away. Without any special threat display the owner will approach, whereupon the trespasser adopts a characteristic posture. With head stretched up, crown feathers raised into a slight peak, and neck looking rather thin, the intruder gives ground and soon flies off, often uttering a tremulous *seep* (a note with a slight trill in it, difficult to transliterate) just as it does so. If two established birds meet at their territorial border their behaviour is very different. They may patrol up and down, side by side, first one and then the other taking a few paces, then perhaps turning and retracing their course. Often such border patrolling takes place day after day along the same section of a territory boundary.

Occasionally the conflict over a territory is not settled by ritualised displays, and the contestants fight. This happens especially at the beginning of the breeding season when competition for territories is most intense and young birds born the previous year are trying to establish themselves. Males usually fight males, and females females, and fights sometimes lead to death. It is not unknown for the victor to continue to peck viciously at the dead body of its victim.

A curious behaviour has been reported, associated with territorial conflicts. A territorial male may pick up and brandish a leaf while engaged in aggressive display against a neighbour or intruder. Some individuals evidently make a habit of doing this, but the behaviour is rare. It is not known whether the brandishing of a leaf helps to intimidate the opponent.

Blackbirds are often aggressive to Song Thrushes, both at feeding places and in the vicinity of their nest. Thus Song Thrushes tend to be prevented from nesting close to a Blackbird's nest, so that if nest sites are in short supply Song Thrushes may be effectively prevented from nesting successfully; they may have to make do with second-rate sites. It is uncertain whether this aggressiveness of

1. The intense aggressive posture of a male Blackbird confronting an equally matched rival. Such displays are seen especially in early spring, when territory boundaries are being established for the breeding season.

2. *Female Blackbird: an old bird with partly yellow bill, yellow eye-rim, and rather dark brown plumage.*

3. *The submissive posture of an unestablished male being expelled from the territory of an established male. Note the sleeked body plumage and peaked crown feathers, in contrast to the aggressive male. Young males, as shown here (dark bill and eye-rim, brownish wing feathers), are often seen in this posture in their first winter and early spring, when they begin to stake out territories of their own.*

the Blackbird has had a long-term effect on the Song Thrush population, but it is well established that the Song Thrush population has declined relative to the Blackbird's since the 1930s.

FOOD AND FEEDING HABITS

Blackbirds are versatile feeders and an extraordinary range of food items has been reported, including slow-worms, tadpoles and small fish taken from streams. But a very large part of their diet consists of two main kinds of food, invertebrates taken from the ground, and fruit. Earthworms make up a large proportion of the invertebrate food, especially at the two seasons when they are most abundant and accessible, early spring and autumn. In hot dry weather worms retreat deep into the soil, and in freezing weather they are generally inaccessible.

Simply by watching a Blackbird foraging for earthworms it is not easy to tell whether it is detecting them by sight or by sound, or perhaps by a combination of both. The foraging bird usually progresses a few steps forward followed by a pause, often with head cocked to one side (which gives an impression of listening).

If it detects a worm it will dart forward a few steps and usually at once pull one from the ground. If the worm is small it may be swallowed straight away; if it is larger it will be mangled, wiped on the ground, and perhaps broken into bits before being eaten. Sometimes a worm is taken to a flower bed or the edge of a path and wiped in dry earth, apparently in order to make its surface less slimy.

However, it seems that Blackbirds and other thrushes hunt for worms by sight. This was demonstrated experimentally in the American Robin, a close relative of the Blackbird. Birds were kept in aviaries, where they could forage for earthworms on the ground. Loud 'white noise' (sound at all frequencies) was played while they foraged, far louder than any sound that could be made by a concealed worm; but birds subjected to this sound were just as successful at finding worms as those birds foraging in silence. Probably Blackbirds and other thrushes are adept at detecting the slight earth movements made by the tip of a worm that is just below the surface or just breaking the surface.

Fruit is eaten at all times of year, but

chiefly in late summer, autumn and winter. The Blackbird, like other thrushes, is what may be called a 'legitimate fruit eater' — that is to say, it eats the fruit in the way that the plant 'wants' its fruit to be eaten, digesting the pulp and voiding the seeds intact, either in the faeces or, in the case of larger seeds, by regurgitation. Thus it acts as a disperser of seeds. In this we may contrast it with fruit eaters that are more accurately called seed predators, which attack fruits in order to eat the seeds, discarding the pulp. Many finches and other birds loosely known as fruit eaters are seed predators. Because they are abundant and eat great quantities of fruit, Blackbirds are important dispersers of their food plants wherever they occur. In New Zealand, where the Blackbird has been introduced and is well established, it is almost certainly the main dispersal agent of a plant that is also introduced, the Black Nightshade.

Nestling Blackbirds are fed on much the same food as the parents eat, earthworms usually being the single most important item. Nestlings of late broods may be fed on caterpillars that fall from the trees in summer, and if they are given them in quantities may temporarily develop a yellow skin, apparently from the yellow pigment in the caterpillars.

When young Blackbirds begin to feed themselves on gaining independence from their parents they are very curious, trying many possible food items in the course of learning which are edible. They seem to have an innate tendency to peck at red objects, and this presumably helps them to exploit fruits, which are often very necessary for them during periods of late summer drought when ground-living invertebrates are inaccessible.

SONG AND CALLS

Most people know the Blackbird's song. It consists of distinct phrases, each one typically about two seconds in duration, separated by pauses. The phrases are varied but unmistakable: they are made up of a few rich flute-like modulated notes and often end with a harsher flourish or chuckle. Each individual male Blackbird has its own repertoire, which develops in complexity in the course of the season. Imitations of extraneous sounds are sometimes incorporated into the song if they are of the right quality. There was a well known case in Germany of a local Blackbird population that incorporated into their songs the habitual four-note whistle used by a man to call his cat indoors; and the author has recorded a Blackbird that at intervals uttered a long series of short ringing whistles, all on the same pitch, copied from a man who regularly whistled to his dogs in this way as he walked through the bird's territory.

Blackbird song usually begins in late winter when the weather is mild. In southern England, if a cold spell ends in mid or late February the warmer weather will release an outburst of song. The first song is generally heard in late afternoon, and gradually it extends back into the earlier part of the day. Dawn song begins a little later. The period of song continues until late June or early July; it ends when nesting is ending. Throughout the main song period, although some song may be heard at any time, individual males have well marked cycles of song. Young males sing persistently when they are establishing their territories; old, established males, by contrast, sing little at this time. When nesting begins, there is at first rather little song at the time of courtship and egg laying. Song increases when the female is sitting on her eggs and then decreases after the young hatch and the male is busy helping to feed them in the nest. As different pairs soon get out of step with one another in their nesting, this cycle is not obvious unless one listens carefully to the song of a known male.

There is some evidence that the Blackbird has been extending its song period in recent decades. It used to be very unusual to hear a Blackbird singing in midwinter; but now it is fairly common to hear occasional song at any time in the winter, but only from Blackbirds living in towns or suburbs. It may be that the provision of food by man enables Blackbirds to maintain a level of physical condition in winter that is not possible for country birds, so that some time can be devoted to advertising their territorial status by song.

Blackbirds have a variety of other calls, each of which is used in particular situa-

4. *Male Blackbird with earthworm, a staple food. A first-year male, showing the brownish flight feathers and outer wing coverts retained from the juvenile plumage but with a fully yellow bill and eye-rim, indicating that it was photographed in the spring or summer following its year of birth.*

5. *Male Blackbird eating ivy berries, an important fruit for thrushes in late winter and spring.*

6. *Male Blackbird bathing, at the moment when the bird dips its head into the water and, with a flicking movement of the wings and shaking of the body, throws a shower of water up over its back.*

7. *Male Blackbird sunbathing. With bill partly open and head and body feathers raised the bird leans away from the sun, fanning the tail and extending the wing on the side facing the sun.*

tions. When slightly excited or mildly alarmed, they utter a subdued *duck, duck.* If the level of excitement is raised, especially in aggressive situations, this changes to the well known chinking call, a loud, repeated *mik mik mik...* This they may utter persistently when they are preparing to go to roost and each bird is staking its claim to a roosting site, often in competition with other birds which, given a chance, might annex it, and also when they are mobbing an owl. Sudden excited alarm, as when a Blackbird is suddenly flushed from cover, is expressed by a loud explosive chatter. A curious note, uttered by dominant birds when advertising their presence in their territory, is a very high-pitched *seeee,* so thin and high that some people cannot hear it. Submissive birds, when they are trespassing and being driven away by the territory owner, give a low-pitched *seep,* as already mentioned, and this call is also used on other occasions as a flight and flight-intention call.

When alarmed by or giving warning against a predator Blackbirds use two very different calls. For ground predators, usually cats in the case of suburban Blackbirds, they utter a low-pitched, rather musical *chook, chook...,* a call that is most often heard when parent birds are looking after fledged young. It has obvious value in not only warning the young of the presence of a predator but also causing them to keep still and silent. For aerial predators, usually hawks, a thin drawn-out *seeee* is uttered, rather like the aggressive *seeee* of territorial birds. Although typically used as warning of an aerial predator, this call should probably be thought of as a more intense anti-predator call, whatever the predator may be; thus shy woodland Blackbirds often utter this call if a human being approaches their nest. A Blackbird that is caught will give loud screaming calls, as many other birds do.

Young Blackbirds have a range of calls that are very different from the adults'. From soon after hatching a nestling utters a faint *yip,* which after a few days gives place to a disyllabic *yi-ip;* basically this is a food-begging call. Later, the begging call turns into a louder, shrilling call, and the *yip* and *yi-ip* are given only between

feeds or after feeding; they appear to indicate satisfaction. After the young have left the nest a new utterance is heard, a harder *chuck* or *chuck-uck,* which enables the parents to locate the fledglings, which spend most of their time concealed in vegetation. As the young become independent, these calls gradually change into calls of adult type.

PAIR FORMATION
AND COURTSHIP.
Old, established Blackbird pairs usually persist from year to year if both members survive. But it often happens that one member of a pair has died, and the population is increased each year by the previous breeding season's young (young Blackbirds breed in their second calendar year, when they are about one year old), so that each year many new pairs are formed. Most are formed around the beginning of the breeding season or in the two months before breeding begins. Earlier, during late autumn and early winter, a male and female may associate quite closely together for a time and may appear to be paired, but these temporary associations break up before the breeding season begins; there is no evidence that firm pairs are formed before January. New pairs may continue to be formed during the breeding season, especially when one member of a pair dies.

Pair formation may be a gradual process or it may be rapid. It is often rapid if the male acquires a territory on or near which an unpaired female is settled, or later in the breeding season when a widowed bird acquires a new mate. It is most often gradual in late winter, when a male and female which have been settled in the same area begin to associate more and more closely and it is hardly possible to say at what point the pair is formed. In some cases the male is aggressive towards the female early in the course of pair formation, treating her like a trespasser in his territory. The female's strategy is to retreat and avoid his attacks but not to leave the territory, and this behaviour usually soon results in her being accepted. When a pair is firmly established the female becomes the dominant partner.

8. *The intense courtship posture of the male (right) and the soliciting posture of the female (left) immediately before mating. Note the similarity of the male's posture to the aggressive posture (figure 1).*

The male Blackbird's courtship display may be performed during pair formation or as a prelude to copulation. It is a striking performance. The head is stretched forward, with crown feathers partially erected and beak open; the neck feathers are compressed and the body feathers fluffed out, especially on the rump, so that the body looks pear-shaped. The tail is fanned and depressed. In this attitude the male parades or postures before the female. If they are on the ground, the male typically bows his head, takes a few steps forward, bows again and then turns and runs back, or he may make more excited movements, jumping up and twirling round between the runs. The whole time, with his beak held open, he usually utters a low, confused song, made up of chattering alarm notes, rough warbles and subdued snatches of typical song. If the birds are in a tree, the male remains stationary or at most occasionally shifts to another perch, and the bowing part of the display becomes more prominent. Various features of courtship display are similar to high-intensity aggressive display, and it may not always be possible to distinguish them, especially in late winter when females may be either potential mates or territorial rivals, unless the circumstances are known and the future course of events is followed.

Courtship displays are associated with the initial stages of pair formation but they are not very frequent; some pairs are formed with little evidence of display. In any case they often take place early in the morning, when few birdwatchers are likely to see them. Later in the breeding season, the display is most likely to be seen being performed by widowed or unpaired males, which are more numerous than unpaired females and so have to court many females before they can find one that is available. (In the breeding season there is a slight excess of male over female Blackbirds, as mentioned later.)

The males of established pairs court their mates only as an immediate prelude to mating. The female, when ready to mate, adopts a soliciting posture, and this stimulates the male to approach in intense courtship posture and then to mount. The soliciting posture of the female is unlike any other posture adopted by the Blackbird. The body feathers are sleeked and the legs are well stretched, so that the bird has a slim, attenuated appearance. The head is raised, with the bill pointing obliquely upwards, and the tail also may be raised or may be held more horizontally. In this posture the female takes little steps to and fro in front of the male, with wings trembling and uttering a strained, low

11

9. *Male Blackbird eating apples in the snow. This photograph shows very clearly the characteristic plumage of a first-winter male; note the brownish flight feathers and the brown fringes to some of the feathers of the underparts.*

volume kind of song with the beak held half open. Mounting is very rapid, hardly taking a second, and for this reason, and also because it takes place mainly in the early morning, it is very seldom seen by the casual observer. Females solicit copulation for only a short period at the beginning of each nesting cycle, from one to five days before the laying of the first egg.

NESTING

The Blackbird's rather bulky cup-shaped nest is built of dry vegetation, strengthened with mud and finished with a lining of dry grasses and other fine stems. The pale greenish eggs are mottled or freckled with brown. They are variable in colour and markings, the ground colour ranging from dull olive-green to pale blue-green and the markings often being

10. *Male Blackbird feeding young. The nestlings are about eight days old, as indicated by the fact that the wing feathers are just beginning to sprout from their sheaths.*

concentrated in a zone at or near the broad end. The nest may be placed at any height from ground level up to 10 metres (35 feet), but the great majority of garden nests, with which most people are familiar, are between 1 and 3 metres (3 to 10 feet). In woodland nests are often placed on or very near the ground, especially at the base of a tree screened by low vegetation. Almost any site may be used as long as it provides a secure base and is reasonably sheltered and concealed. In towns and suburbs buildings are often used, a ledge inside an open shed or barn being especially favoured.

In southern England Blackbirds usually begin to prospect for nest sites in mild weather from late February onwards (further north, breeding tends to be a little later). Both male and female prospect, often in company, and a great number of possible sites may be visited by the pair. The female tends to prospect more assiduously, hopping with deliberate movements through bushes and creepers, occasionally crouching as if testing the suitability of a site, probably the firmness of its base and its outlook. Sometimes the male appears to show a possible site to his mate, who goes to inspect it immediately after he has visited it. It is apparently the female who makes the final choice.

After a few days of prospecting the female begins to pick up nest material, and soon afterwards she begins to build. Males also occasionally peck at and even pick up and carry nest material, but they have never been reliably reported to help to build the nest. Nest building is a slow, almost leisurely process at the beginning of the breeding season, carried out mainly in the morning in mild, damp weather, and it may be two weeks before the nest is complete. Later in the season nests may be built much more quickly, sometimes in as little as two days, and such nests are much less substantial than the early ones. A new nest is usually built for each brood — or, more accurately, for each nesting attempt, as nestings often end in failure; occasionally a nest is re-used after a little refurbishment, but only if the previous nesting has been successful and the nest has stayed in good condition. In practice the only nests that remain in good enough condition are those in sheltered sites, especially in niches on buildings or inside buildings.

The eggs, nearly always three to five in number, are laid daily, usually between 7 a.m. and noon. The female begins to incubate gradually, while the clutch is still incomplete. A study of birds nesting in captivity showed that she starts to turn the eggs soon after laying, about every other hour for the first day and then hourly. By the time the last egg is laid she spends about 90 per cent of the daylight hours on the nest, and all night. The male does not incubate, but he takes an interest in the nest during incubation and may go to it when the female is away feeding and stand guard over it, or may even crouch in the nest-cup. This behaviour has given rise to reports that male Blackbirds sometimes incubate, but they certainly never do so in normal circumstances. However, apparently reliable reports have indicated that if the female is killed or is absent for an unusually long time, the male may sit on the nest; but as he lacks an incubation patch (the vascularised patch of bare skin with which the female transfers heat to the eggs) his attempts at incubation are unlikely to be successful.

Because incubation begins gradually, before the clutch is complete, the eggs hatch over a period of a day or two; the period for each egg is about thirteen days. The intimate details of hatching and the female's care of the nestlings just after hatching have been seen only in birds breeding in captivity, but they are probably no different in the wild. The female cleans the young soon after hatching and may help weak nestlings to get free from the shell. During the first few hours she feeds the young on saliva and keeps the male away from the nest. Later both parents feed the young. The male's contribution is the greater while the young are small, as the female spends much time brooding them. She broods them almost continuously for the first three or four days, and then decreasingly until by the age of eight or nine days she covers them only at night or in bad weather. After the first few days male and female feed the young about equally. Both parents also see to the sanitation of the nest. They remove faecal pellets as the young void them, either swallowing them or later, when the young are large, flying off with them and dropping them well away from the nest. If a small nestling dies in the nest, as quite often happens, a parent removes it, carrying it away and dropping it near the edge of the territory. If, however, a nestling dies after the age of about nine days, a rarer occurrence, it is too large to remove and remains in the nest.

In suburban habitats, where nesting Blackbirds are most likely to be watched, earthworms are the staple food of the young. But in deciduous woodland, which must be closer to the Blackbird's ancestral habitat, caterpillars are an important food for the young; at times very large numbers fall from the trees to the woodland floor, where they are collected by foraging Blackbirds. Adult insects are also important, especially in the latter part of the breeding season when dry weather often reduces the availability of earthworms; and fruit is regularly fed to large nestlings.

Blackbirds have several ways of guarding their eggs and young against predators. The male may warn his mate, when she is on the nest, by uttering the high-pitched alarm *seeee,* or sometimes by giving low-volume song. If a predator approaches when there are young in the nest, the parents give warning *chook* calls, which cause the young to keep still and silent. A predator such as a Jay may be attacked by the parent Blackbirds, which may even grapple with it and fall to the ground interlocked. Very tame female garden Blackbirds may be especially bold in defence of the nest against a human intruder. They may refuse to budge from the nest and peck hard at an outstretched hand, or if they are off the nest they may attack in flight, coming in from behind and striking the intruder on the head with a foot as they fly past. Distraction displays, which some birds use as their chief means of protecting their young against predators, are rarely used by Blackbirds, but very occasionally a female may land on the ground and run to and fro in a crouched posture in an attempt to lure a human intruder from the nest. Male Blackbirds seldom, if ever, use these stratagems against human intruders, but they may attack small mammals that approach the nest.

Like all songbirds, nestling Blackbirds grow fast. They hatch, sparsely covered with down and with their eyes closed, at a weight of about 6 grams (0.2 ounce). When they leave the nest, usually at an age of thirteen or fourteen days, they weigh about 70 grams (2.5 ounces). Their eyes open at an age of about eight days. At seven days the first feathers of the juvenile plumage, which succeeds the natal down, begin to burst from the feather sheaths, and by nine or ten days the young bird appears well feathered. They begin to show fear at an age of about seven days, crouching silently in the nest if disturbed; at about nine days they begin to scream when handled, and a day or so later handling by man or any other disturbance will cause them to leave the nest prematurely. This behaviour is infectious; the screaming of one nestling causes the others to start scrambling out, and once this has happened it is difficult to get them to settle back in the nest again. Although at this age the young seem still very helpless, it must usually be safer for them to leave the nest prematurely than to stay in it and almost certainly fall victim to the predator (not man, of course, but the behaviour was evolved before civilised man was on the scene). The author once carelessly caused a family of young Blackbirds to leave the nest prematurely at the age of ten days. They survived well, at least three out of the four being alive eight days later.

If the nest is undisturbed the young usually leave spontaneously, when thirteen or fourteen days old. They remain in thick cover for about a week and then begin to move out into the open, often hopping to meet a parent when it approaches with food. The young are fed by one or both of the parents for about three weeks after leaving the nest. Towards the end of the dependent period there is a gradual transition from being wholly dependent on the parents for food to finding most of it for themselves. At this time young birds tend to show alternating adult and juvenile behaviour: after a spell of foraging for itself more or less successfully, a young bird will suddenly stop, look up and, uttering begging calls, hop off in search of a parent.

Blackbirds are among the small number of bird species in which it has been found that the two parents divide the family after fledging, the male caring for some of the youngsters and the female for the others. The division may take place as soon as the young have left the nest, or not for several days. After division, not only does each parent feed only its 'own' young and ignore the others, but the young themselves learn to beg only from the parent which is feeding them. This behaviour is seen most clearly in late broods, when the female does not begin another nest. When the female re-nests, she usually hands over the whole family to the male at the time of division, or she may continue to feed one or two of them. If she continues to feed some of her family her next nesting tends to be delayed. Exceptionally, she may be still feeding young from a previous brood while incubating her next clutch of eggs.

Statistical aspects of breeding

Garden Blackbirds usually lay their first eggs in March, and their last eggs in May or June. Occasional birds start earlier than this, or continue later; and exceptionally mild weather may stimulate occasional pairs to breed well in advance of the normal season, especially in towns where the local microclimate is warmer than in the country. In the course of the three months or so of breeding one nesting attempt follows another in close succession. Most females make two, three or four attempts in the course of a season; and the most successful may rear three, or exceptionally even four, fami-

11. *Blackbird nest with eggs. The mud strengthening the cup is concealed by an inner lining of dry vegetation. Blackbird eggs are quite variable; these are typical, as is the size of the clutch, which may range from two to six eggs but is most commonly four.*

12. *Male Blackbird removing a faecal sac after feeding its young. The well feathered nestlings are nearly ready to leave the nest. Note the traces of nestling down still adhering to the tips of the newly grown head feathers.*

lies. Females that are breeding for the first time tend to have shorter seasons than older females, beginning a little later and ending earlier. The weather affects the length of a season at both ends. Nesting begins late in a cold spring, and it ends earlier than usual if the early summer weather is very dry. Probably because of the differences in local climate, woodland Blackbirds begin to nest a week or two later than garden Blackbirds. As would be expected, there are geographical differences, the breeding season being slightly later in the north than in the south of Britain.

The clutch size is affected by many factors. Most clutches are of three to five eggs, but there is a small proportion of two-egg and six-egg clutches. The main variation is seasonal: the average clutch-size rises and then falls in the course of the breeding season. Early in the season three or four eggs are usually laid. Occasional clutches of five are laid at the end of March, but clutches of five are not common until the second half of April. As the clutches of five increase, clutches of three decrease. The rise continues until just after mid May; thereafter the average clutch size falls rapidly, until by the end of June most clutches consist of three eggs. The few clutches of six are laid during the peak period, from the end of April to the beginning of June. In addition to the seasonal variation there is further variation due to habitat, weather

17

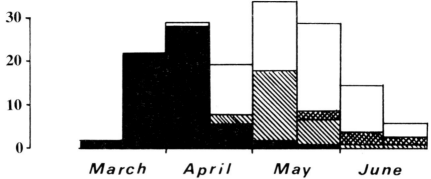

13. *The Blackbird breeding season at Oxford, showing all nestings of 59 pairs over four years and based on the date on which the first egg of each clutch was laid. The black area of the histogram indicates first clutches, the diagonally shaded area indicates second clutches (after successful fledging of the first family), and the cross-hatched area indicates third clutches (after successful fledging of two families). The unshaded area indicates all clutches laid after a previous failure.*

and the age of the female. Thus clutches tend to be higher in woodland than in towns and suburbs; in the early part of the season they tend to be higher in warm weather than in cold weather, and old females tend to lay larger clutches than females breeding for the first time. There is also, superimposed on all this, geographical variation: clutch sizes are on average larger in the north than in the south, and a little larger, at corresponding latitudes, in the east than in the west. It is probable that all these kinds of variation are adaptive, that is, that they enable each female to lay the number of eggs that corresponds to the number of young she and her mate are most likely to be able to rear successfully. Thus conditions for feeding and rearing a family are best in the middle part of the breeding

14. *Seasonal variations in average clutch size of Blackbirds in southern England, based on over three thousand records in the archives of the British Trust for Ornithology. Clutches may vary from two to six eggs, but most are of three to five eggs. Further details are given in the text.*

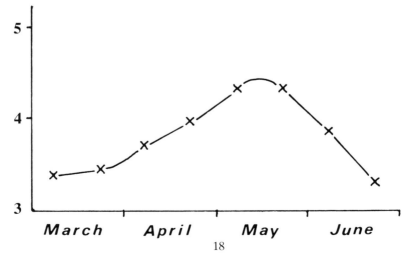

season; day length is longer in the north than in the south, so that there is more time to feed a large family; and old females are better able to rear a large family than young females.

Blackbird nests are subject to all kinds of hazards. They may be attacked by a predator, be deserted as a result of disturbance, succumb to unseasonal weather, or collapse because they are badly sited; or the parents may be unable to find enough food for the young, which may die. Nevertheless, about one half of garden nests succeed in producing young to the fledging stage. Woodland nests are considerably less successful, mainly because they are much more liable to predation; a study in an oakwood near Oxford showed that only 14 per cent of the nests were successful.

Populations and movements

The Blackbird is one of the most abundant of British birds, if not the most abundant. As a breeding bird it is almost ubiquitous, occurring in nearly every one of the 10 km grid squares into which Britain and Ireland are divided; only in a few squares consisting of bare mountain or moorland is it absent. The breeding population has been estimated at over 7 million pairs, which makes it possibly

15. *A ringed Blackbird before release. The numbered rings, issued by the British Trust for Ornithology, identify the bird individually and if it is caught again, or found dead, give information on its movements and length of life.*

16. *Female Blackbird feeding a fledged youngster. The fledgling has its tail about two-thirds grown, indicating that it has been out of the nest for about ten days. Note the pale shaft streaks on the feathers of the back and wing coverts. The juvenile plumage is replaced in late summer or autumn, except for the tail, flight feathers and outer wing coverts, which are not replaced until the late-summer moult of the following year.*

more numerous than its main contenders for the title of most abundant land bird (such estimates make many assumptions and may not be very accurate). The only species that may perhaps outnumber it are Chaffinch (about 7 million pairs), Starling (4 to 7 million pairs), and House Sparrow (3½ to 7 million pairs). Because of the influx of migrant Blackbirds from northern Europe, details of which are given below, the winter population must be even larger; a rough estimate suggests a figure of around 20 million individuals.

The movements and migrations of Blackbirds in Britain are very complex. Some local populations are highly sedentary. For instance, from an intensive four-year study of an Oxford garden population of between eleven and seventeen pairs, during which nearly all the adults and all the young that were produced were ringed — some five hundred birds in all — there was no evidence that any bird moved more than 2 miles (3 km)

from where it was ringed. This may be normal for Blackbird populations of rich garden habitats in southern England, but some British-born Blackbirds are migratory. About 2 percent of those ringed as nestlings in southern England have been recovered in a subsequent winter in Ireland, and another 2 per cent from continental Europe south or south-east of England, mainly from France. It may be that these migratory individuals were from habitats less favourable for wintering in than Oxford gardens are, but this is not known. Blackbirds born in northern England and Scotland are much more migratory: the percentages of those that have been recovered in Ireland are, respectively, about 15 per cent and 30 per cent. Only one of these north British birds has been recovered in continental Europe.

In addition to these overseas movements, a proportion of British-born Blackbirds migrate considerable dis-

17. *Movements of British-born Blackbirds in their first autumn and winter, based on recoveries of ringed birds. The thick arrows are a selection from a large number of records of movements to Ireland; the thin arrows constitute all recorded movements to the continent up to 1965. Note that the directions taken by northern birds (a little south of west) are very different from the southerly directions taken by birds from southern England. Birds born in the area enclosed by the broken line probably have a 'choice' between migrating to Ireland or south to the continent. These long-distance migrants are only a small fraction of the British Blackbird population, most birds being sedentary.*

18. *Movements of British-born Blackbirds in their second and later winters (conventions as figure 17). Note that the directions taken are much more varied than in the first winter, and birds migrate to Ireland from a more extensive area of England and Scotland. There is some movement within Ireland in the course of the winter, towards the very mild south-west of the country.*

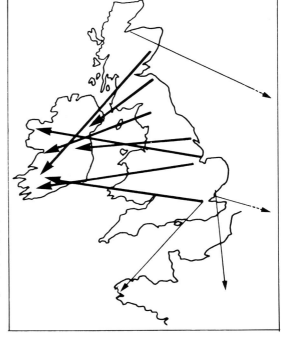

tances within Britain in their first autumn, and surprisingly there is a strong tendency for the movement to be in a north-westerly direction. Thus a bird born in the south midlands may spend its first winter in north Wales. In later winters, movements within Britain tend to be in a more southerly direction.

Ringing has shown that the proportion of young British Blackbirds which migrate overseas in their first autumn is the same as the proportion of older birds which migrate. This is surprising, as on the continent ringing has shown that many Blackbirds which migrate in their first autumn remain resident in later winters, and there seems to be another difference between British and continental birds. In northern continental Europe it has been found that more female Blackbirds migrate than males, but the evidence indicates that among British Blackbirds both sexes are about equally likely to migrate. Although hundreds of thousands of Blackbirds have been ringed, and many thousands have been recovered, there are many details of their complex movements and migrations that remain to be sorted out.

In winter Britain's breeding Blackbird population is augmented by large numbers of birds from northern continental Europe. They begin to arrive on the east coast in September, but the main influx is in October. They soon spread all over the country and many continue to Ireland, whose southern and western coastal areas, with their very mild climate, provide what is probably the most favourable wintering habitat for thrushes in the whole of Europe. There large numbers accumulate, especially in severe weather. It is puzzling that many counts of wintering Blackbirds, in Ireland and elsewhere, have all tended to show a male to female ratio of about 3:2, although, with more continental females migrating than males, any imbalance would be expected to be in favour of females. Where local breeding populations have been studied closely, a slight excess of males has been noted.

The immigrant Blackbirds are mainly from the population breeding in Scandinavia and Germany, and in recent years an increasing number has been coming from Finland and Russia. It is probable that this eastward extension of the area of origin of the migrants results from the fact that Blackbirds have been increasingly colonising gardens in Finland and Russia. The adaptation of Blackbirds to urban and suburban habitats is a gradual process, which is still continuing. Garden Blackbirds are much more likely to be ringed, and found dead, than woodland Blackbirds. Most of the recoveries showing this eastward extension are of birds ringed in Britain in winter and found dead in the breeding season in Finland and Russia.

Longevity and mortality

In captivity a Blackbird has been known to live for twenty years. From ringing, it is known that wild Blackbirds may live at least sixteen years. But this potential age, of twenty years or more, must be reached only by a minute proportion of the Blackbirds that reach adulthood. The annual mortality of adults is about 33 per cent, which means that after ten years only about 2 per cent of the original adult population will be still alive.

Blackbirds, like all small British songbirds, breed when they are a year old. If the population is to remain more or less steady, with a 33 per cent annual mortality rate, each pair must each year contribute on average only about 0.7 of a bird to the following year's breeding population. In an intensively studied Oxford garden population, each pair produced an average of 4.1 young per year to the fledging stage, and of these about 1.7 per pair survived until the next breeding season. Hence this population, which there was no reason to think untypical of garden populations, was producing more young than were needed to replace its losses. Other populations — perhaps those in more natural habitats where predators are more numerous — may well tend to under-produce. There is no evidence for any major change in the level of the British Blackbird population over recent years.

As young Blackbirds do not disperse far before trying to acquire a territory, a consequence of the over-production of young in the Oxford population was that there was intense competition for space, and some birds failed to acquire a suitable territory for what should have been their first breeding season. This was particularly the case for males. For some reason (perhaps because young females suffered heavier mortality in their first autumn and winter and so were less numerous by the start of their first breeding season), all or nearly all young females acquired a mate and, with the mate, a breeding territory in their first year; but a floating population of unestablished males remained. Hence established males whose mates died in the course of the breeding season either took a long time to acquire a new mate or in many cases remained unmated for the rest of the season, but widowed females very quickly obtained new mates. It is not known whether this is the general situation in Blackbird populations elsewhere, but it seems likely to be so.

Although it might be thought that winter is the hardest time of the year for Blackbirds (and other birds), most Blackbird deaths occur in the breeding season, at least in garden populations. This is probably a consequence of the stress of acquiring and holding a territory, and of the fact that breeding birds are at increased risk when attending nests and young. Thus in a sample of 348 Blackbirds ringed as nestlings in Britain and found dead in subsequent years, 55 per cent died in the four months March to June. This may be a common mortality pattern for birds living in suburban and urban habitats; it has been found, for example, that 54 per cent of House Sparrow deaths occur during its breeding season (April to July).

The Blackbird and man

The sight of a tame Blackbird feeding in a suburban back garden would have been surprising to our ancestors. Thomas Bewick, writing in 1804, described the Blackbird as 'a solitary bird, frequenting woods and thickets'. Later nineteenth-century writers describe it as nesting in woodland but in winter frequenting the neighbourhood of houses and even coming into towns. By the end of the nineteenth century it seems to have become as thoroughly suburbanised as it is today. Its spread into the centre of large cities took place early in the twentieth century. Clearly, Blackbirds became more and more tolerant of man as man became more tolerant of Blackbirds, and especially as suburban man gave up his ancient role of hunter; but another essential factor in the change was that man-made habitats, especially gardens, provided Blackbirds with excellent conditions for both feeding and nesting. In other parts of the Blackbird's range the colonisation of towns and suburbs is even more recent. As we have already seen, in north-east Europe it is still going on. In south-east Europe the Blackbird is still mainly a bird of the wooded mountains, and man there is still very much a 'hunter' of any bird large enough to be worth eating.

Man has had an even more dramatic effect on the Blackbird's range. Blackbirds were introduced into Australia and New Zealand in the nineteenth century. Where the climate is suitably mild and humid they have done well. In New Zealand not only have they spread all over the large islands but in addition, apparently unassisted by man, they have colonised all the main outlying islands. Blackbirds are now among the commonest of New Zealand birds and, as we have seen, have probably been the main dispersers of the seeds of an introduced plant, the Black Nightshade. Their success in New Zealand and south-east Australia (the humid part of the continent, where they have done well) must have been helped by the fact that there are no native thrushes, so that they had no native competitors in exploiting the garden habitats which there, as in Britain, are so well suited to their needs.

Further reading

Batten, L. E. 'Population Dynamics of Suburban Blackbirds'. *Bird Study* 20, 251-8 (1973).

Hall-Craggs, J. 'The Development of Song in the Blackbird *Turdus merula*'. *Ibis* 104, 277-99 (1962).

Lack, D. *Population Studies of Birds*. Oxford University Press, 1966.

Nicholson, E. M. *Birds and Man*. Collins, 1951.

Simms, E. *British Thrushes*. Collins, 1978.

Snow, D. W. *A Study of Blackbirds*. Allen and Unwin, 1958.

— 'The Migration and Dispersal of British Blackbirds'. *Bird Study* 13, 237-55 (1966).

— 'Long-distance Movements of British Blackbirds'. *Ringing and Migration* 2, 52-4 (1978).

Spencer, R. 'Changes in the Distribution of Recoveries of Ringed Blackbirds'. *Bird Study* 22, 176-90 (1975).

ACKNOWLEDGEMENTS

All photographs are reproduced by courtesy of the Frank Lane Picture Agency. They are acknowledged to: John Hawkins, 9, 10; Peggy Heard, 7; Eric and David Hosking, cover and 2, 4, 6, 11, 12, 15, 16; C. Newton, 5. Other illustrations are by the author.